A Whole Book Of THINGS I LOVE ABOUT US

1

You're into

____.

I'm into

____.

Yet somehow, we make it work.

2

Our shared love for

____

knows no bounds.

3

If they gave out awards for

____,

we'd definitely win.

4

Together,
there's nothing we can't

____.

Except for maybe

____.

5

I love watching

____

with you.

6

I love how much you make me

____

when you

____.

7

I sometimes find myself daydreaming about our

________________________________.

8

If we had a reality show,
it would be called

____.

9

I love how we make
each other feel so

______________________________.

10

I don't even mind
when we argue about

______________________________.

(You're still wrong, though.)

11

Nobody else will ever truly understand our feelings about

______________________________.

12

I love it when we share

______________________________________.

13

I even tolerate it when we share

______________________________.

(This is big!)

14

We bring out the

____

in each other.

15

Between your

____

and my

______________________________,

we could survive the
zombie apocalypse.

16

Promise me that someday we'll

____

together.

17

Being with you makes
me want to be a better

____.

18

I love how good we are
at giving each other

________________________________.

19

If we were an article
of clothing, we'd be

__________________________________.

20

It probably annoys
other people when we

______________________________________.

(Whatever.)

21

At any given time,
we're most likely to be

____.

22

In the movie version of our life,
we'd be played by

____

and

____________________________________.

23

Everyone should be as

____

as we are.

24

I still can't believe we

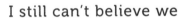

____.

25

And how is it possible
that we've never

_____________________________________?

26

I love how we could

____

all day.

27

If we could just stop

____

we'd be

______________________________.

28

I secretly want us to

______________________________________.

(Oops, not a secret anymore!)

29

We just

____

together so well.

30

May our

____

last to infinity.

I LOVE

US!

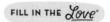

FILL IN THE *Love*®

Created, published, and distributed by Emily McDowell & Friends
11111 Jefferson Blvd. #5167
Culver City, CA 90231
emilymcdowell.com
Emily McDowell & Friends is a trademark of Knock Knock LLC
Fill in the Love is a registered trademark of Knock Knock LLC

Printed in China

ISBN: 9781642446654
UPC: 812729027158

10 9 8 7 6 5